Tom Johns...

Year 1995

Cartoons from the
News of the World **and**
The Sun

The Prince's Nightmare

ORION

First published in 1995 by
Orion

An imprint of Orion Books Ltd
Orion House, 5 Upper St Martin's Lane
London WC2H 9EA

A CIP catalogue record for this book is available
from the British Library

ISBN: 0 75280 293 3

Printed and bound in Great Britain by
Guernsey Press Co. Ltd, Guernsey C.I.

"When I asked you to blow ... I meant into this bag!"

"Whatever happened to the magic sponge?"

"It's on the table ready and waiting for him!"

"A present for you Myra ... Fred West's chair!"

"... and all this time we thought he was just talking to the plants!"

"Letting a journalist interview him ... spilling more royal scandal ... and his valet is just as bad!"

"Well, for a start ... he can't talk!"

"Mam! … it's the gasman!"

"... and another great kick by Cantona!"

Tom Johnston

"I don't care how much publicity Diana got ... change it!"

Tom Johnston

"Hold your fire ... it's just an electricity boss!"

8 February 1995

John Major revealed to have had older girlfriend in his youth

Tom Johnston

"I've come to ask your advice about having affairs with older women!"

12 February 1995

Paula leaves Bob

"I don't like Sundays!"

13 February 1995

Cantona kicks out on holiday

"... and I hear that Cantona is staying at this hotel!"

"Please tell me you snatched him!"

16 February 1995

England fans riot in Dublin

"It's Jacques Santer ... he's had a sudden change of heart about opening the borders!"

"I caught him climbing over the wall ... to get inside!"

Tom Johnston

19 February 1995

"That's right, sarge ... I'm afraid some real England fans found him first!"

21 February 1995

Princess Diana has secret meetings with art dealer

"Don't worry ... it's just that ruddy Oliver Hoare again!"

"We're really worried about our Graham ... says he wants to be a Tory MP when he grows up!"

Tom Johnston

BARINGS BANK

POSITION CLOSED

POSITION CLOSED

28 February 1995

Barings staff lose
jobs after collapse
and rescue

3 March 1995

The artist formerly known as ...

Tom Johnston

"All I said was I'm going to make a bomb!"

7 March 1995

Britain's oldest bank collapses

"Yes, but who said anything about you coming back as bosses!"

"Besides a power boss, a supermodel and a derivatives whizzkid ... is there any other work you'd like to do?"

"He swings both ways!"

"Oy, chummy! ... You forgot to leave your key with reception!"

"The Governor is worried you might have keys!"

"Do you think it's some kind of omen?"

15 March 1995

Police investigate
soccer corruption
allegations

"How much is it worth for us to drop John Major?"

"Careful, officer! ... I'll have you know I'm a friend of Fergie's!"

PUTNEY

Tom Johnston

"He's celebrating his vote of confidence victory!"

21 March 1995

INXS lead singer steals
Bob Geldof's wife

"Who was the scruffy, Irish bloke who wired the sound?"

"Have you got a copy of 'The Economist'?"

"Oh, Mr. Churchill! ... there's someone to see you!"

28 March 1995

Frozen embryos date stamped

"He was born 40 years after he was conceived!"

Tom Johnston

"'Ere, Mum, Dad! look at these great flowers I nicked off some geezer's grave!"

"Right! Now point out his bit on the side!"

2 April 1995

Tories criticise radio interviewer for his aggressive technique

"It's more ferocious than a pit-bull, mate ... it's a John Humphreys!"

4 April 1995

The recession hits the high street

"Nobody ever thinks about all the unemployed bank robbers!"

"It's Camilla's son ... are you growing anything he can smoke?"

"Quick! ... let's elect a new captain!"

7 April 1995

Virginia Bottomley moved from the Health ministry in Cabinet shuffle

"I'm closing you down!"

Tom Johnston

9 April 1995

"Don't shoot! ... It's Camilla's son!"

10 April 1995

MP Dick Spring
caught out

"Isn't it marvellous? ... spring has come at last!"

"... So they all rolled over and one fell out ..."

13 April 1995

"Looks like the crime rate is going up again!"

"But Tony ... I thought we were supposed to copy the Tories!"

Woman in her fifties has late baby

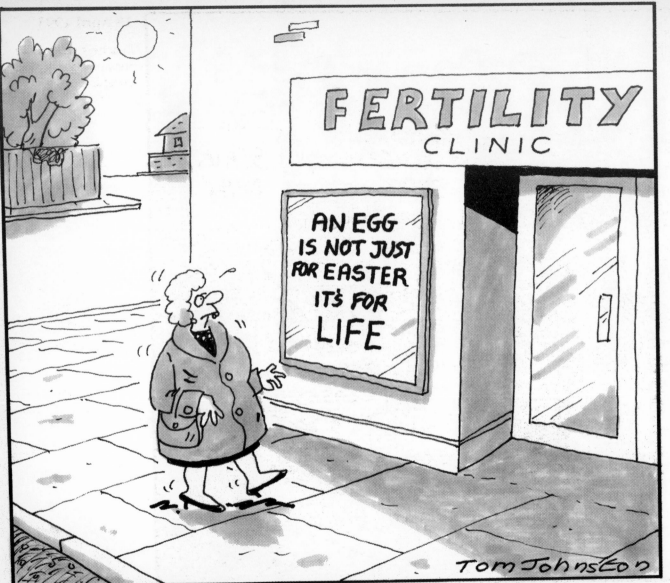

18 April 1995

Teachers strike over new examination structure

"It wasn't a good idea to let the kids make our signs!"

"Let's start with me taking a look at your drivers' license!"

"Tell my teacher? ... I am the teacher!"

21 April 1995

EC bans strawberry for not conforming to standards

"You're blowing the wrong kind of raspberry!"

"Got to keep these pervs out of the Army, eh Eva?"

26 April 1995

Newsagent in lottery
scratchcard fraud

"It was you!"

"Yeah! He's lucky ... he's got a rich, popstar brother!"

28 April 1995

Lottery fund buys
Churchill's speeches
for millions

Tom Johnston

"It's the lottery ... they've bid 87p for your speeches!"

"Norma! Have you seen my papers anywhere?"

Tom Johnston

2 May 1995

Camilla Parker Bowles to divorce

"No! We're not interested in buying … we just wanted to see the room they bonked in!"

Tom Johnston

Tories desperate for
local election victory

"Oy! This is *my* pitch for begging!"

7 May 1995

"... defeated and dejected, the final surrender was near ..."

Tom Johnston

Tom Johnston

9 May 1995

VE Day celebrations
bring thousands to
London

VE DAY
HYDE PARK →

"'Ere! Let's mug that old age pensioner!"

"I bet they don't drink Carling's black label!"

"Just keep Desmond Lynam away from the female javelin throwers!"

Tom Johnston

"Would someone remove that man from the line?"

"... but you said you wanted the kind of face that will get you on the telly!"

"I'd like a refund!"

19 May 1995

"We'll have to build an extension for the Conservative Party!"

"Oh yes! That's Imran's love child all right!"

Soldiers accused
of drug taking at
Windsor Castle

"Wrong turn, Angus!"

"Oh my god! ... It's Betty Boothroyd!"

"What do you mean you're mounting a leadership challenge?"

"My husband cleverly moved his national grid shares into my name ... then I left him!"

28 May 1995

Page 3 girl splits from husband

"Ah! Here comes Linda Lusardi's husband!"

"Someone here wants to join the party!"

31 May 1995

Soldiers take UN hostages in Bosnia

"Who's idea was it to capture the British troops?"

1 June 1995

Fergie claims poverty in *Hello* magazine

TOM JOHNSTON

"Well, we had to help her out, didn't we?"

"The gas shareholders finally caught up with him!"

5 June 1995

MP Sir Nicholas Scott
has road accident

"Anything you say will be taken down and used to win Labour the election!"

"This is a prescription for headache pills!"

7 June 1995

Did Waldegrave mislead the government over arms to Iraq?

"I've just mislead him into thinking he won't have to resign!"

8 June 1995

Charities miss out in lottery handouts as donations go down

"It's not you!"

9 June 1995

Holidaymaker
has affair with
construction
workers

"But darling! ... they remind me of our Spanish holiday!"

"Evening! ... I'm your new vicar!"

"No! I didn't give the order for Nicholas Scott to get Lord Justice Scott!"

Tom Johnston

13 June 1995

"He's really embarrassed about losing the rugby to England!"

15 June 1995

Prince William accepted at Eton

Tom Johnston

"Tell the new boy his mum's here to pick him up from school!"

"It's you!"

"Forget the lottery! ... how about I just libel you?"

20 June 1995

Mastermind winner come tv presenter in sex scandal

Tom Johnston

"I had that Fred Housego in the back of his cab once!"

22 June 1995

Failed suicide spends days halfway down a cliff

25 June 1995

"My Cabinet are one hundred per cent behind me!"

"Sorry ... I'm afraid we haven't got a leader I could take you to!"

"Here come the cling-ons!"

29 June 1995

Film star, Hugh Grant, arrested in Los Angeles

"In a movie, officers ... in a movie"

"It's either an earthquake or Hugh Grant"

7 July 1995

Ageing Stones rock-on
in UK tour

Tom Johnston

**"I can't decide whether to go to the Queen Mum's birthday outing or
the Rolling Stones concert!"**

"Stay where you are or I'll call the police!"

"Not tonight dear ... I've got a writ!"

16 July 1995

Elizabeth Hurley
furious over her film
star lover's arrest

"Besides that, Hugh ... how did Liz take it?"

24 July 1995

Record hot summer
brings the super-wasp

"So, who's complaining?"

"... 'til another scandal in the Sun do you part ..."

"It's either a fatcat or Ian Brady on a prison outing!"

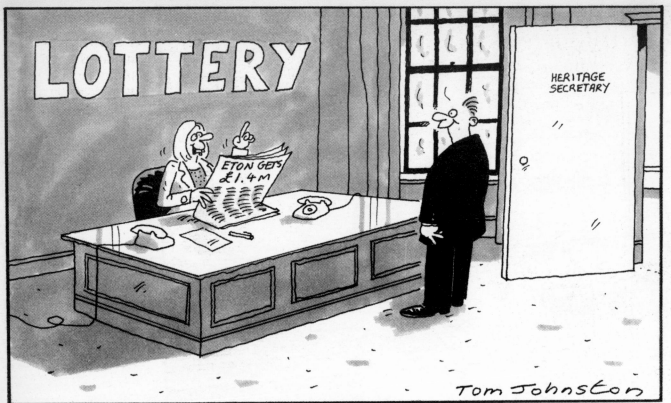

"The royal family is part of our heritage ... let's give them a few million!"

"Mr Suggins will be taking over your job for the price of a Giro!"

"If that's Princess Diana again, tell her to leave me alone!"

Tom Johnston

"Yeah! Well he was only in for manslaughter!"

"Now we know the truth ... it's where he keeps his wallet!"

11 August 1995

"I guess I shouldn't have made those comments about new Labour being ruthless!"

"I'm sorry madam but I don't think Princess Diana *would* be interested in stealing your husband"

"It's Diana's 'never say sorry' outfit!"

"Are we really on an eighteen hole course or are we just Broadmoor
inmates playing crazy golf?"

18 August 1995

The long hot summer rages on as privatised water boards impose bans

"We're hoping to get Michael Barrymore's autograph!"